Olim
Once upon a time... IN LATIN

READER I

CONCEIVED & WRITTEN

BY MARY ELLEN TEDROW-WYNN

EDITED BY SUSAN SCHEARER

COVER & LAYOUT DESIGN BY LYDIA FRANK

TYPESETTING BY ALLISON ARMERDING

ILLUSTRATIONS BY RACHEL SCHANZENBACH

About the Author

Mary Ellen Tedrow-Wynn is the mother of seven children and has been schooling at home for more than 20 years. Helping others find appropriate, affordable books has been her love since she began the journey herself. You can contact her with questions or comments at the website listed below.

We have triple-checked for errors in this text. However, should you notice any mistakes, we would love to hear from you. Please contact us at *laurelwoodbooks@earthlink.net.*

Ōlim Reader I
Laurelwood Books © 2015
ISBN: 978-1-941383-03-2

Find this and other great books on our website:
www.laurelwoodbooks.com

You may also reach us at:
Laurelwood Books
1639 Ebenezer Road
Bluemont, VA 20135

How to use this Reader:

Ōlim, Once Upon a Time...in Latin uses fables, parables, and Bible stories to gently introduce young children to Latin.

- A Fable is a short story, usually with animals as characters, conveying a moral.
- A Parable is a simple story used to illustrate a moral or spiritual lesson told by Jesus in the Bible.
- A Bible Story retells an event that occurred in the Bible.

Our stories are presented in simpler English to facilitate the translation into very simple Latin. Begin with the English version to give the student a taste of the story. Some children will already know the story and that is great!

The story is then presented completely in Latin, just as it was in English. Latin-English vocabulary is given in a sidebar on every page to help you and your student. Read the Latin version through several times for better retention.

Read a page in the Reader, then do the corresponding pages in the workbook. You can do a page a day or more, to suit the pace of your student. The workbook correlates page by page to the reader, and will help the student retain more than reading through the reader alone. There is an answer key provided in the workbook to ensure comprehension.

A younger sibling reader is also available. The child learning Latin should read this to a younger sibling or friend. This will give your student more practice with the vocabulary while gently exposing another child as well!

And now...Happy Reading!

How to Pronounce Latin

a	ah	the first syllable of "aha"	
with a macron, twice as long, as in 2nd syllable of "aha"			portābat
ae	eye	as in "line"	Graeciae
au	ow	as in "how"	causa
b	b	normal English	
c	k	as in "kick"	Cicero
d	d	normal English	
e	eh	as in "met"	
	with a macron: AY as in "make" or "day"		petēbat
ei	AY	as in "make" or "day"	deinde (NOT de-inde)
eu	eoo	as in "you" (but without the strong "y"); "ew, that stinks!"	Eurōpa
f	f	normal English	
g	hard g as in "game" (NOT as in "germ")		gerere
h	breathe out Latin considers this neither a vowel nor a consonant		
i + consonant OR inside a word: ih, as in "hit"			
	with a macron: EE as in "feet"		dīcit
i followed by a vowel at the beginning of a word			
	"y" as in "yard"		iam
j	sometimes used for "i followed by a vowel at the beginning of a word"		Jūlius = Iūlius

k	used only in Latin words borrowed from Greek; pronounced as English "k"		
l, m, n	normal English		
o	as in "port"		
	with macron "oh" as in "hello"		optō
oe	oy	as in "toy"	foedus
p	p	normal English	
qu	kw	as in "quick"	quisque
r	r	normal English	
s	s	as in "see" (NO "z" sound)	Āsia
t	t	normal English	
u	uh	as in "us"	
	with macron "oo" as in "shoe"		Iūlius
ui	wi	as in "queen"	cui
		(yes, this sounds just like quī)	
v	w	as in "with"	Salvē
w	did not exist in Latin		
x	ks	normal English	
y	euh	somewhere between a short "i" and a short "u"	Syra
z	did not exist in Latin; borrowed from Greek's zeta, as in zephyrus.		

Pronunciation, cont.

Pronounce double letters TWICE:

"cc" as in "kicK Kings"

"ff" as in "ofF First"

"gg" as in "doG Game"

"ll" as in "alL Lost"

"mm" as in "I'M Messy"

"nn" as in "oN Nothing"

"pp" as in "uP Periscope"

"ss" as in "aS Seems"

"tt" as in "ducT Tape"

Syllables and Accents:

A syllable is determined by having a vowel or diphthong (2 vowels pronounced as one, as in ae, au, ei, eu, oe, ui: see the list above)

The third-to-last syllable is the antepenult.

The next-to-last syllable is the penult.

The last syllable is the ultima.

Accent the penult in a two-syllable word: *Amat*

Accent the penult in a 3-or-more-syllable word IF the penult

1) has a macron: *puelLĀrum*

2) OR ends in two consonants: *puELla*

Otherwise accent antepenult: AMbulat

Roman Numerals

I = 1
II = 2
III = 3
IV = 4
V = 5
VI = 6
VII = 7
VIII = 8
IX = 9
X = 10
XI = 11
XII = 12
XIII = 13
XIV = 14
XV = 15
XVI = 16
XVII = 17
XVIII = 18
XIX = 19
XX = 20
XXI = 21
XXII = 22
XXIII = 23
XXIV = 24
XXV = 25
XXVI = 26
XXVII = 27
XXVIII = 28
XXIX = 29
XXX = 30
XXXI = 31
XXXII = 32
XXXIII = 33
XXXIV = 34
XXXV = 35
XXXVI = 36
XXXVII = 37
XXXVIII = 38
XXXIX = 29
XL = 40
XLI = 41
XLII = 42
XLIII = 43
XLIV = 44
XLV = 45
XLVI = 46
XLVII = 47
XLVIII = 48
XLIX = 49
L = 50
LI = 51
LII = 52
LIII = 53
LIV = 54
LV = 55
LVI = 56
LVII = 57
LVIII = 58
LIX = 59
LX = 60

The Three Little Pigs

Once upon a time...

...there were three little pigs.

It was necessary to go out into the world. Mother said, "Be wise!"

The first little pig was foolish. He saw a man who carried straw and he said, "Give me straw. I want to build my house."

And the first little pig built his house.

Soon a big, bad wolf came. The wolf said, "Little pig, little pig, I want to come in."

The first little pig answered, "No way!"

The wolf huffed and puffed and he blew down the house. Then he ate the little pig.

The second little pig was also foolish. He saw a man who carried big sticks. He said, "Give me some sticks. I want to build my house."

Then the second little pig built his house.

Soon the big, bad wolf came. The wolf said, "Little pig, little pig, I want to come in."

The second little pig said, "No way!"

The wolf huffed and puffed and blew down the house.

Then he ate the second little pig.

The third little pig was wise. He saw a man who was carrying bricks.

He said, "Give me bricks. I want to build my house." Then he built his house.

Soon the big, bad wolf came. He said, "Little pig, little pig, I want to come in."

The third little pig said, "No way, foolish wolf!"

The wolf huffed and puffed. He blew again-and again. Nothing happened. He was not able to blow down the house.

He shouted, "I want to come in!"

Still nothing happened. The wolf climbed up onto the roof. He wanted to go down through the chimney and capture the pig, but the pig saw him.

In the house, the pig had hot water in a pot on the fire. The wolf fell into the hot water.

The big, bad wolf never again bothered the wise little pig.

Trēs▷ Parvī▷ Porcī

Vocabulary

Ōlim . . . . Once upon a time

erant . . . . there were

trēs▷ . . . . three

parvus▷ . . . . } small
parva▷ . . . . or
parvum▷ . . . . little

porcī . . . . pigs

necesse erat . . . . it was necessary

exīre . . . . to go out

in . . . . into

mundum. . . . . world

māter . . . . mother

dīxit . . . . . . (he, she, it) said

este prūdentēs. . . . . be wise

Key

▷ . . . . adjective
▫ . . . . direct object

lim...

erant trēs▷ parvī▷ porcī.

Necesse erat exīre

in mundum.

Māter dīxit,

"Este prūdentēs▷."

STOP Do Workbook Exercise I

Prīmus▷ porcus parvus▷ erat stultus▷.

Vīdit virum▫ quī portābat strāmentum▫ et dixit, "Dā mihi strāmentum▫. Volō aedificāre vīllam▫ meam▷."

Et primus▷ porcus parvus▷ aedificāvit vīllam▫ suam▷.

Vocabulary

prīmus▷	first
erat	was
stultus▷	foolish
vīdit	he saw
vir, virum	man
quī	who
portābat	carried
strāmentum	straw
et	and
dā mihi	give to me
dā	give
mihi	to me
volō	I want
aedificāre	to build
meam▷	my
vīlla, vīllam	house
aedificāvit	built
suam▷	his

Key

▷ .... adjective
▫ .... direct object

STOP Do Workbook II & III

Vocabulary

mox . . . . soon

magnus▷ . . . . big

lupus . . . . wolf

malus▷ . . . . bad

vēnit . . . . came

dīxit . . . . said

parve▷ porce . . . . . little pig

volō . . . . I want

intrāre . . . . to come in

respondit . . . . answered

nūllō modō . . . . no way

Key

▷ . . . . adjective

▫ . . . . direct object

Mox magnus▷ lupus malus▷ vēnit.

Lupus dīxit, "Parve▷ porce, parve▷ porce, volō intrāre."

Prīmus▷ porcus parvus▷ respondit, "Nūllō▷ modō!"

Do Workbook Exercise IV

Lupus inflābat,

et exflābat,

et dēflāvit vīllam[▫].

Tum vorāvit porcum[▫]

parvum[▹].

STOP Do Workbook Exercise V & VI

VOCABULARY

inflābat. . . . . huffed (inhaled)

exflābat . . . . puffed (exhaled)

dēflavit. . . . . . . .blew down

tum . . . . then

vorāvit . . . . .he ate

KEY

▹ . . . . .adjective

▫ . . . . .direct object

VOCABULARY

secundus▷ . . . . second

quoque . . . . also

vidit . . . . he saw

qui . . . . who

magna bacula▫ . . . big sticks

Dā . . . . Give

mihi. . . . .(to) me

volō. . . . . .I want

aedificāre . . . . .to build

aedificāvit . . . . built

KEY

▷ . . . . adjective

▫ . . . . direct object

Secundus▷ porcus parvus▷ quoque erat stultus▷.

Vīdit virum▫ quī portābat magna▷ bacula▫ et dīxit, "Dā mihi bacula▫. Volō aedificāre vīllam▫ meam▷."

Tum secundus▷ porcus parvus▷ aedificāvit vīllam▫ suam.

Do Workbook Exercise VII

Mox magnus▷ lupus

malus▷ vēnit.

Lupus dīxit, "Parve▷ porce,

parve▷ porce, volō intrāre."

Secundus▷ porcus parvus▷

dīxit, "Nūllō▷ modō!"

VOCABULARY

mox . . . . soon

magnus▷ . . . . big

malus▷ . . . . bad

dīxit . . . . . . (he, she, it) said

volō. . . . . I want

intrāre . . . . to come in (enter)

nūllō modō. . . . . no way

KEY

▷ . . . . adjective

▫ . . . . direct object

STOP Do Workbook Exercise VIII & IX

VOCABULARY

lupus . . . . wolf

dēflāvit . . . . blew down

vīllam . . . . house

tum . . . . then

vorāvit . . . . he ate

secundum▷ . . . . second

KEY

▷ . . . . adjective

▫ . . . . direct object

Lupus inflābat et exflābat

et dēflāvit vīllam.▫

Tum vorāvit secundum▷

porcum▫ parvum▷.

 Do Workbook Exercise X

Tertius▷ porcus parvus▷ erat prūdēns▷. Vīdit virum▫ quī portābat laterēs.▫

Dīxit, "Dā mihi laterēs▫. Volō aedificāre vīllam▫ meam."▷

Tum aedificāvit vīllam▫ suam.▷

STOP Do Workbook Exercise XI & XII

VOCABULARY

tertius▷ . . . . third

prūdēns▷ . . . . wise

laterēs . . . . bricks

dīxit . . . . he said

dā mihi . . . . give me

volō . . . . I want

aedificāre . . . . to build

aedificāvit . . . . built

vīllam suam▷ . . . . his house

KEY

▷ . . . . adjective

▫ . . . . direct object

VOCABULARY

mox . . . . soon

vēnit . . . . .came

verberāvit. . . . . knocked

ianuam . . . . door

volō. . . . . .I want

respondit . . . . answered

lupe stulte▷ . . . foolish wolf

KEY

▷ . . . . adjective

▫ . . . . .direct object

Mox lupus vēnit.

Verberāvit ianuam.▫

Dīxit, "Parve▷ porce,

parve▷ porce,

volō intrare!"

Tertius▷ porcus parvus▷

respondit, "Nūllō▷ modō,

lupe stulte▷!"

STOP Do Workbook Exercise XIII & XIV

Lupus inflābat et exflābat.

Flāvit rūrsus et rūrsus.

Nihil accidit. Nōn poterat

dēflāre vīllam.[□]

Clāmāvit, "Volō intrāre!"

Rūrsus nihil accidīt.

STOP Do Workbook Exercise XV

Vocabulary

et . . . . and

rūrsus . . . . again

nihil . . . . nothing

accidit . . . . happened

clāmāvit . . . . he shouted

nōn poterat . . . . he was not able

dēflāre . . . . . to blow down

flāvit . . . . . (he, she, it) blew

Key

▷ . . . . adjective

□ . . . . direct object

VOCABULARY

ascendit . . . . climbed up

tēctum . . . . roof

voluit . . . . he wants

dēscende. . . . . . to go down

per. . . . . through

caminum . . . . chimney

capere. . . . . to capture

vīdit. . . . . he saw

sed. . . . . but

eum. . . . . him

KEY

▷ . . . . adjective

▫ . . . . direct object

Lupus ascendit in tēctum.

Voluit dēscendere per caminum et capere porcum▫ sed porcus vīdit eum.▫

STOP Do Workbook Exercise XVI

In vīllā porcus habēbat aquam calidam▷ in ollā in igne. Lupus cecidit in aquam calidam.▷

Magnus▷ lupus malus▷ numquam rūrsus turbāvit porcum▫ parvum▷ et prūdentem▷.

STOP Do Workbook Exercise XVII & XVIII

VOCABULARY

in vīllā	in the house
habēbat	had
aquam▷ calidam	hot water
in ollā	in the pot
in igne	in the fire
cecidit	fell
numquam	never
rūrsus	again
turbāvit	bothered

KEY

▷ .... adjective
▫ .... direct object

The Tortoise and the Hare

Once upon a time...

there was a hare who praised himself all the time. He said, "I will run very fast. No one will run faster."

The tortoise did not want to hear the hare.

The tortoise challenged the hare to a race.

The hare laughed. It will be easy to overcome the tortoise.

The race excited the other animals in the forest. The race started.

The tortoise was very slow. He took one slow step. Then another. Then a third.

The hare was very fast.

He looked back. He saw the very slow tortoise. He decided to sleep.

When he opened his eyes, he saw the tortoise near the end.

The hare ran very quickly, but the tortoise was first!

A slow and steady journey always wins.

Testūdō et Lepus

Vocabulary

testūdō .... tortoise
et .... and
lepus .... hare
Ōlim .... Once upon a time
erat .... there was
quī .... who
laudābat .... praised
sē .... himself
semper .... all the time
dīxit ...... (he, she, it) said
curram .... I will run
rapidissimē .... very fast
nēmō .... no one
curret .... will run
rapidius .... faster

Key

▷ .... adjective
▫ .... direct object

Ōlim...

erat lepus quī laudābat sē▫ semper.

Dīxit, "Curram rapidissimē, nēmō curret rapidius."

STOP Do Workbook Exercise I

Testūdō nōlēbat audīre leporem▫.

Testūdō prōvocāvit leporem▫ ad cursum.

STOP Do Workbook Exercise II & III

VOCABULARY

testūdō . . . . tortoise

nōlēbat . . . . . . did not want

audīre . . . . to hear

leporem▫ . . . . hare

prōvocāvit . . . . . challenged

ad cursum . . . . . (to a) race

KEY

▷ . . . . adjective

▫ . . . . direct object

Vocabulary

rīsit . . . . laughed

erit . . . . .it will be

facile▷. . . . . easy

superāre . . . . . to overcome

testūdīnem▫ . . . . . tortoise

excitābat . . . . excited

cētera▷ . . . . other

animālia . . . . .animals

silvā. . . . . forest

Key

▷ . . . . adjective

▫ . . . . .direct object

Lepus rīsit. Erit facile▷ superāre testūdīnem▫.

Cursus excitābat cētera▷ animālia▫ in silvā.

STOP Do Workbook Exercise IV

Cursus initium▫ fēcit.

Testūdō erat tardissima▷.

Fēcit ūnum▷ tardum▷ gradum▫.

Tum alterum▷.

Tum tertium.

STOP Do Workbook Exercise V & VI

VOCABULARY

cursus . . . . .race

initium . . . . a beginning

erat . . . . was

tardissima. . . . . . . very slow

fēcit. . . . . (he, she, it) made (took)

ūnum▷ . . . . one

tardum▷ . . . . slow

gradum▫ . . . . .step

tum . . . . then

alterum▷ . . . . another

tertium▷ . . . . .a third (step)

KEY

▷ . . . . adjective

▫ . . . . .direct object

VOCABULARY

rapidissimus......very fast

respexit...(he) looked back

vīdit.............. he saw

tardissimam▷....very slow

cōnstituit ...... he decided

dormīre.......... to sleep

KEY

▷ ....adjective

▫.............direct object

Lepus erat rapidissimus.

Respexit. Vīdit

tardissimam▷ testūdīnem▫.

Cōnstituit dormīre.

STOP Do Workbook Exercise VII

Cum lepus aperuit oculōs,▫

vīdit testūdīnem▫ prope

fīnem.

Lepus cucurrit rapidissimē

sed testūdō erat prīma▷!

Iter lentum▷ et cōnstāns▷

cursum superat▫.

STOP Do Workbook Exercise VIII & IX

VOCABULARY

cum . . . . when

aperuit . . . . opened

oculōs . . . . eyes

prope . . . . near

fīnem . . . . end

cucurrit. . . . . .he ran

rapidissimē. . . .very quickly

sed. . . . . but

prīma▷ . . . . .first

iter . . . . .journey

lentum▷ . . . . slow

cōnstāns▷. . . . . steady

semper . . . . always

superat . . . (he, she, it) wins

KEY

▷ . . . . adjective

▫ . . . . direct object

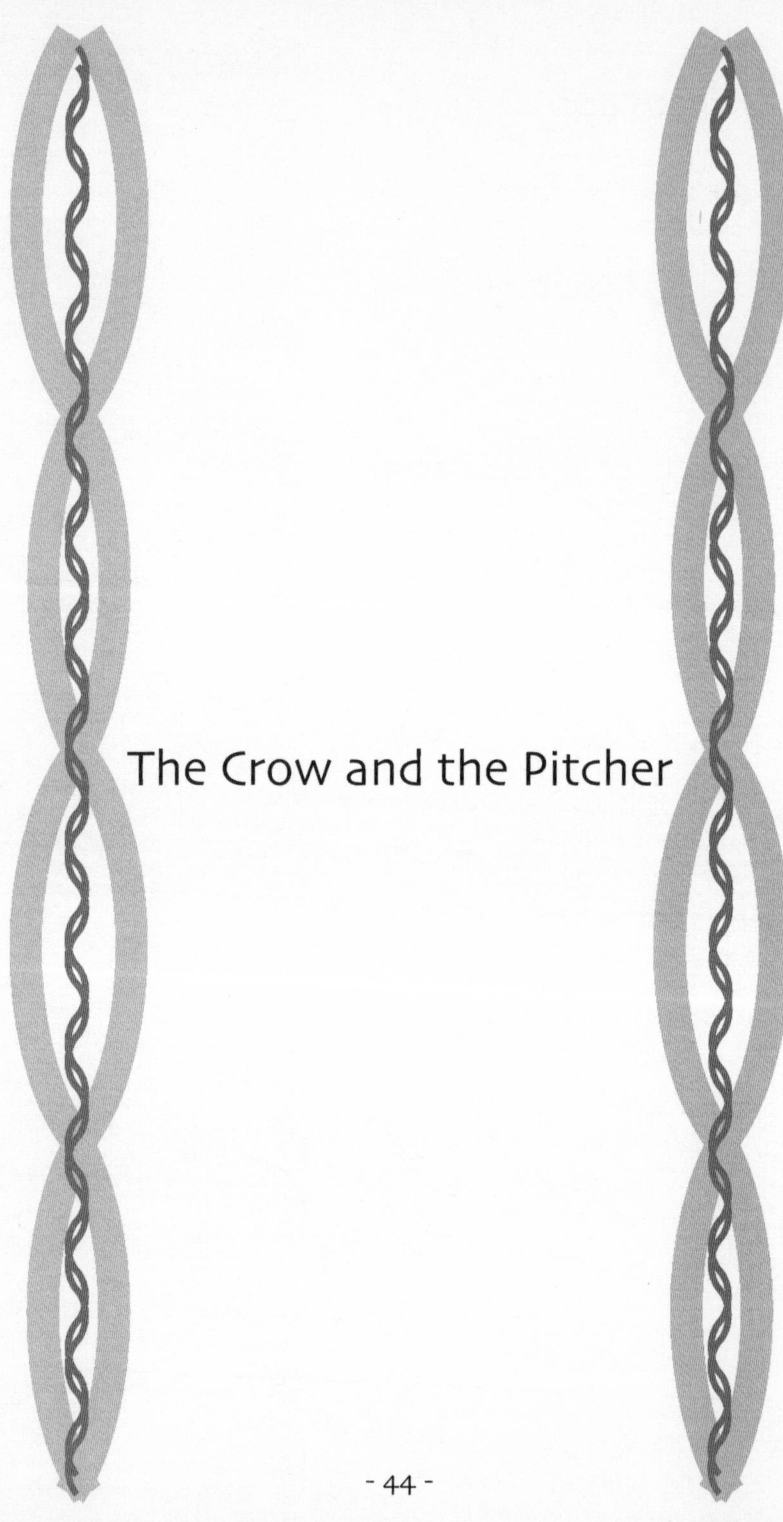

The Crow and the Pitcher

Once upon a time...

there was a crow who wanted very much to drink water. He wanted to find water.

He found a pitcher and was happy.

Behold! Water!

But there was a small amount in the pitcher. The water was not high enough. Therefore, the crow was not able to drink the water.

Was the crow discouraged? No, the crow was not discouraged!

He was not able to break the pitcher. The pitcher was too strong!

The crow wanted to *turn upside down the pitcher. The pitcher was too heavy!

Was the crow discouraged? No, the crow was not discouraged!

* Author's note: We know that this is odd phrasing. We want to keep these words together because all three words make one word in Latin.

Finally, he found pebbles.

He dropped one pebble into the pitcher.

Then he dropped another, and a third.

At last, the water came to the top. Now the crow was able to drink.

He was happy!

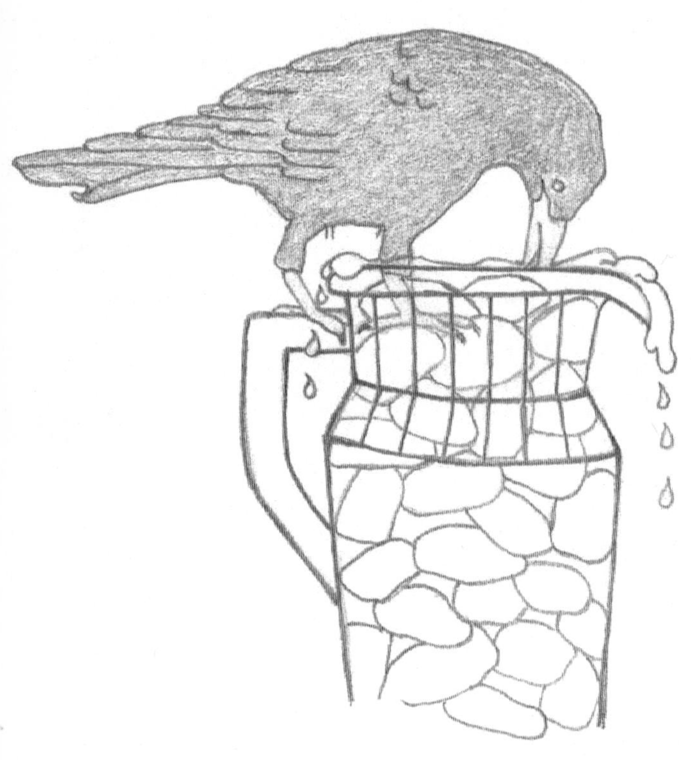

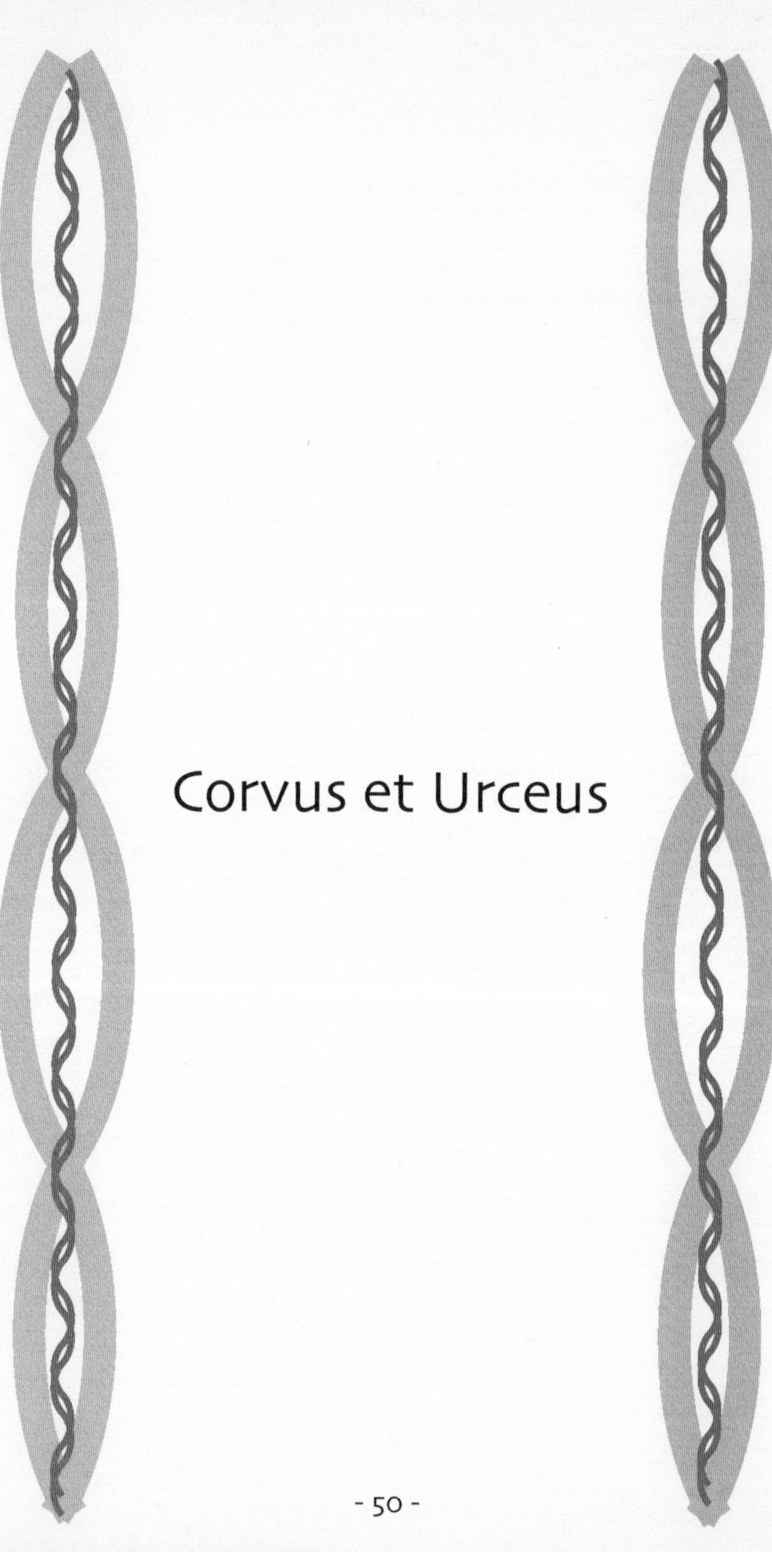

Corvus et Urceus

lim...

erat corvus quī volēbat maximē bibere aquam□.

Volēbat invenīre aquam□.

Invēnit urceum□ et erat laetus▷.

STOP Do Workbook Exercise I

Vocabulary

ōlim. . . . . once upon a time

erat . . . . .there was

corvus. . . . . .crow

quī. . . . . who

volēbat . . . . he wanted

maximē. . . . . very much

bibere . . . . to drink

invēnire . . . . to find

aquam□. . . . . water

invēnit . . . . he found

urceus, urceum□ . . . pitcher

laetus▷ . . . . .happy

Key

▷ . . . . .adjective

□ . . . . .direct object

Vocabulary

ecce . . . . behold

aqua . . . . water

sed . . . . but

paulum . . . . . small amount

aquae . . . . of water

in urceō . . . . in pitcher

Key

▹ . . . . adjective

▫ . . . . direct object

Ecce! Aqua!

Sed erat paulum aquae in urceō!

STOP Do Workbook Exercise II & III

Aqua nōn erat satis alta▷.

Itaque corvus nōn poterat bibere aquam▫.

Eratne corvus afflictus▷?

Minimē! Corvus nōn erat afflictus▷!

STOP Do Workbook Exercise IV

VOCABULARY

nōn erat . . . . was not

satis. . . . . enough

alta▷ . . . . high

itaque . . . . therefore

nōn poterat . . . was not able

aquam▫. . . . . water

eratne . . . . was he

afflictus▷ . . . . .discouraged

minimē . . . . no way

nōn afflictus. . . . . not discouraged

KEY

▷ . . . . adjective

▫ . . . . direct object

Vocabulary

poterat . . . . was able

nōn poterat . . was not able

frangere . . . . to break

nimis . . . . too

fīrmus▷ . . . . strong

Key

▷ . . . . adjective

▫ . . . . direct object

Nōn poterat frangere urceum▫.

Urceus erat nimis fīrmus▷.

STOP Do Workbook Exercise V & VI

Tum volēbat ēvertere urceum▫.

Urceus erat nimis gravis▹!

Eratne corvus afflictus▹?

Minimē! Corvus nōn erat afflictus▹.

STOP Do Workbook Exercise VII

VOCABULARY

tum . . . . then

ēvertere . . . . to turn upside down

gravis▹ . . . . heavy

nimis . . . . too

KEY

▹ . . . . adjective

▫ . . . . direct object

Vocabulary

postrēmō .... finally

invēnit .... he found

calculōs□ .... pebbles

calculum□ .... pebble

dēmīsit .... he dropped

ūnum▷ .... one

in .... into

et .... and

alterum▷ .... another

tertium▷ .... third

Key

▷ .... adjective

□ .... direct object

Postrēmō invēnit calculōs□.

Dēmīsit ūnum▷ calculum□ in urceum.

Tum dēmīsit alterum▷ et tertium▷.

STOP Do Workbook Exercise VIII & IX

Postrēmō aqua pervēnit ad summum urceum.

Nunc corvus poterat bibere.

Erat maximē laetus▷!

STOP Do Workbook Exercise X

VOCABULARY

pervēnit. . . . . .came

ad summum urceum . . . . . . to the top of the jug/pitcher

urceum . . . . . of the pitcher

poterat . . . . was able

nunc . . . . now

bibere . . . . to drink

maximē. . . . . . . .very much

laetus▷ . . . . happy

KEY

▷ . . . . adjective
▫ . . . . direct object

Items available from Laurelwood Books:

Ōlim, Once Upon a Time, in Latin Series:
Ōlim Workbook I (companion to Ōlim Reader I)
Book II (reader and workbook): The Ant and the Chrysalis, The Lost Sheep, The Good Samaritan
Book III (reader and workbook) - The Feeding of the 5,000, The Lion and the Mouse
Book IV (reader and workbook) - Creation
Book V (reader and workbook) - Daniel, Part I; We Know a Tree by its Fruit
Book VI (reader and workbook) - The Prodigal Son
book VII (reader and workbook) - David and Goliath
Book VIII (reader and workbook) - Daniel, Part II
Book IX (reader and workbook) - Daniel, Part III, The Miser
Book X (reader and workbook) - The Wise Man and Foolish Man, The Ten Maidens

Patriotic Penmanship Series for Grades K-12
Also Available: Jump Rope Review Book, Transition to Cursive Book, Dinosaur Review Book

State The Facts: A Guide to Studying Your State
Whether you are studying the state you live in or any other state, this book offers your student the opportunity to research and learn state history, geography, weather, and more!

Study Guides:
Based on Rosemary Sutcliff's historical fiction:
The Eagle of the Ninth • The Silver Branch
Outcast • The Lantern Bearers
Warrior Scarlet • Sword Song • The Shining Company

Based on Emma Leslie's historical fiction:
Out of the Mouth of the Lion
Glaucia the Greek Slave

Laurelwood Books offers both new and used curricula to families wishing to help their children learn and achieve success in school or at home.

To order: www.laurelwoodbooks.com
laurelwoodbooks@earthlink.net